English

Key Stage 2
For ages 9-10

Practise & Learn

Published by CGP

Editors:
Luke Antieul
David Broadbent
Anthony Muller
Jo Sharrock
Rebecca Tate

Updated by Izzy Bowen, Emma Cleasby, Alex Fairer and Holly Robinson.

With thanks to Glenn Rogers for the proofreading.

ISBN: 978 1 84762 733 9

Printed by Elanders Ltd, Newcastle upon Tyne
Clipart from Corel®

Contents

Commonly Confused Words

Homophones are words that are pronounced the same, but have different spellings and meanings.

scent and sent

Fill in the homophones and then find all the words in the wordsearch.

steal ➡ S T E E L

herd ➡ ☐☐☐☐

guessed ➡ ☐☐☐☐☐

altar ➡ ☐☐☐☐☐

aisle ➡ ☐☐☐☐

```
D I D H E R D A G
E L S D S S F W U
S R S L U T A D E
S A A E E E E R S
E H L T V E W A T
U A T L L L T E L
G P E N U A E H T
E A R N A I S L E
```

Write a sentence using each of these words.

past ➡ I walk past the park every day. ....

passed ➡ ....

allowed ➡ ....

aloud ➡ ....

Find homophones for each of the words below.

led ➡ L E A D

serial ➡ ☐☐☐☐☐☐

farther ➡ ☐☐☐☐☐☐

prophet ➡ ☐☐☐☐☐☐

draft ➡ ☐☐☐☐☐☐

mourning ➡ ☐☐☐☐☐☐☐

Some verbs and nouns have very similar spellings, but they mean different things.

advise and advice

The verb usually ends with -ise.

The noun usually ends with -ice.

I would **advise** you not to go there.
My **advice** is — do not go there.

Write the words below on the correct clipboard.

verbs

license

licence   ~~license~~

devise   device

practise   practice

prophecy   prophesy

nouns

Fill in the gaps by using the correct verb or noun from the box.

| advise / advice | devise / device | practise / practice | ~~license~~ / licence |

1 The medical council decided to ..... license ..... the doctor.

2 Before you can drive a car, you need to get a driving ....

3 Marvin liked to .... his football skills in the park.

4 You have to do a lot of .... to become a professional juggler.

5 I .... you to stay away from the abandoned funfair.

6 My granny gives good .... when I have a problem.

7 The super-villain decided to .... an evil plan.

8 A mobile phone is an example of an electronic hand-held ....

Word Endings

Sometimes words sound similar, but are spelled differently.

| incred**ible** | and | veget**able** | | horr**ibly** | and | toler**ably** |

Words ending in -ible and -able sound similar.

Words ending in -ibly and -ably also sound similar.

Cross out the bold word in each sentence below that is spelled incorrectly.

1. Arnold finally achieved the **impossable** / **impossible** and caught his tail.

2. Eve's slice of cake was **considerably** / **consideribly** larger than Anna's.

3. The bike my parents bought for me has an **adjustible** / **adjustable** seat.

4. My brother was **visibly** / **visably** scared of my tarantula.

5. The boy crossed the road **sensibly** / **sensably** on the way to school.

6. The island is only **accessable** / **accessible** on foot when the tide is low.

Finish the words in the sentences using **-able**, **-ible**, **-ably** or **-ibly**.

1. The hamsters were so ador.................... that we bought three.

2. My dad told me it was irrespons.................... to lie to my brother.

3. Faruq won the cycling race comfort....................

4. When I write quickly, my writing is illeg....................

5. Mrs Burrows, my piano teacher, is very depend....................

6. The friar was terr.................... pleased when the rain stopped.

7. It was debat.................... whether the outlaw was a hero.

The endings **-ant** and **-ent** both sound like 'unt'. ⟹ participant frequent

resistance obedience ⟸ The endings **-ance** and **-ence** both sound like 'unce'.

The endings **-ancy** and **-ency** both sound like 'uncy'. ⟹ hesitancy emergency

The endings **-ent**, **-ence** and **-ency** usually come after **soft 'c'** sounds, **soft 'g'** sounds and **'qu'**, but there are lots of exceptions.

Add **-ant** or **-ent** to the words below to spell them correctly.
Write the completed words on the correct clipboard.

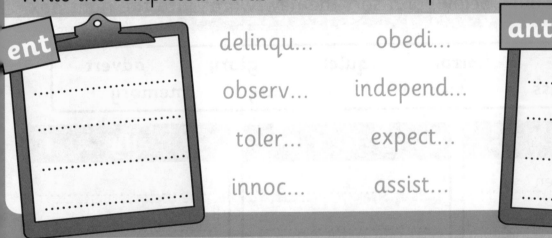

ent

delinqu...   obedi...

observ...   independ...

toler...   expect...

innoc...   assist...

ant

Choose the correct ending to complete the sentences.

| ance | ence | ancy | ency |

1. She had the dec............ to apologise for taking my pen without asking.

2. He helped an elderly man who needed assist............ crossing the road.

3. Zara felt full of confid............... the night before her swimming gala.

4. The restaurant had a job vac............... for a new chef.

5. The thief pleaded his innoc............... to the judge.

6. The mysterious subst............... could only be one thing — alien goo!

7. "Don't adjust the radio frequ...............!" warned the police chief.

Changing Word Types

You can add a suffix to the end of a word to make nouns or adjectives into verbs. You sometimes have to change the spelling of the root word.

Noun to **Verb**

liquid ⟹ liquid**ise**

Adjective to **Verb**

active ⟹ activ**ate**

Adding **-ise**, **-ify** and **-en** can turn nouns into verbs. Add the correct suffix to the nouns below, and sort the new words into the right box.

~~fright~~	horror	quiet	glory	advert
class	strength	summary	memory	

en	ise	ify
frighten	....	....
....	....	....
....	....	....

Choose the correct suffix to make the adjectives below into verbs.

ify	ate	ise	en

Using step-by-step instructions can ....*simplify*.... a difficult task. ⟹ **simple**

Madha performed a silly dance to .... the mood. ⟹ **light**

Abe didn't .... before stepping out onto the stage. ⟹ **hesitant**

I let the jelly .... before serving it. ⟹ **solid**

Moe and Joe .... in digging tunnels. ⟹ **special**

First, ... the butter in a saucepan. ⟹ **soft**

Prefixes

A prefix can be added to the start of a word to change its meaning.

un + graceful = **un**graceful   **dis** + graceful = **dis**graceful

Even though both words have the root word 'graceful', adding a prefix changes the meaning.

Add either **re-** or **mis-** to complete the sentences
below and match the meaning in brackets.

1) Jack ....placed his phone. (Jack lost his phone.)

2) Jack ....placed his phone. (Jack bought a new phone.)

3) Tim ....read the instructions. (Tim read the instructions wrongly.)

4) Tim ....read the instructions. (Tim read the instructions again.)

One sentence below uses the prefix **dis-**, the other uses the prefix
re-. Explain the difference in meaning between the two sentences.

1) The mayor was disappointed after the council's decision.

....

2) The mayor was reappointed after the council's decision.

....

Write a sentence containing each of the words on the left.

dislike ⟹ I dislike most vegetables. ....

unlike ⟹ ....

devalued ⟹ ....

undervalued ⟹ ....

9

Degrees of Possibility

Some adverbs show how possible or certain something is.

> Dan will **probably** play basketball this afternoon.

Tick the sentence that is the **most certain**.

Lucy is surely the best dancer in the group. ☐

Lucy is possibly the best dancer in the group. ☐

Lucy is probably the best dancer in the group. ☐

Rewrite the sentences, replacing the underlined adverbs with an adverb that's **less certain**. Use a different adverb in each sentence.

1 There will <u>definitely</u> be something to eat at the party.
There will probably be something to eat at the party.

2 <u>Surely</u> Toshiko and Elliot are going to be late for school.

....

3 <u>Clearly</u> Meera is going to win the prize.

....

Rewrite the sentences, replacing the underlined adverbs with an adverb that's **more certain**. Don't reuse the same adverb.

1 <u>Maybe</u> we should teach Natalie how to play tennis.

....

2 We will <u>possibly</u> need to buy some bread in the morning.

....

Modal verbs also show how certain or possible something is. They're used to give more information about the main verb in a sentence.

I **will** go to the beach.

modal verb   main verb

I **might** go to the beach.

'might' shows that going to the beach is possible, but not certain.

Circle the modal verb in each of the sentences below.

1 We may go to the park.

2 You could try the library.

3 He can meet you tomorrow.

4 I might be late.

5 Peter will help you find the bag.

6 After my swim, I shall eat lunch.

7 Sue should be here by now.

8 You must not run in the classroom.

Tick the sentence that is **the most certain**.

Anya might take the shoes back to the shop tomorrow.

Anya shall take the shoes back to the shop tomorrow.

Anya may take the shoes back to the shop tomorrow.

Anya should take the shoes back to the shop tomorrow.

Circle the modal verb in each sentence which is **less certain**.

1 Josiah might / must ride his bike tomorrow.

2 We will / could go and visit our grandma.

3 I can / may take the dog for a walk.

4 I should / must tidy my room tonight.

5 The brave princess says she shall / could fight the terrible dragon.

Punctuation for Parenthesis

Commas, brackets and dashes can all be used to separate extra information in a sentence. ⇐ The extra information is called a parenthesis.

My neighbour, **who is very friendly**, waved to me.

I took Frankie **(my border collie)** for a walk on the beach.

Alison — **who is an astronaut** — boarded a rocket to Mars.

Tick the sentences which use dashes correctly.

Sarah — the village vicar — plays the electric guitar. ☐

My favourite dessert — chocolate — ice cream is lovely. ☐

The dog — who was excited — barked happily. ☐

In the town where — I live — there's a windmill. ☐

Add a pair of brackets to each sentence below.

1. I went to the pool the one with the water slide yesterday.

2. My brother who loves driving bought a black sports car.

3. Gavin the local farmer shaved his llama.

Add commas to the correct places in the passage below.

My brother who is a gardener was kidnapped by the world's most famous pirate Captain Nancy Locket last year. He was forced to join the crew of her ship the fearsome Maroon Destroyer and learn to be a pirate. He soon came face to face with Captain Fourbeards Captain Nancy's arch-enemy during a sea battle. The Maroon Destroyer's crew defeated Captain Fourbeards and took his ship the Barber's Fortune as a prize.

Commas

Some sentences can be read in more than one way.

> The girl who is in charge of training Dhriti is our best striker.

This sentence is ambiguous — its meaning isn't clear.

You can use commas to avoid confusion and make a sentence clearer.

A girl, who is training another girl called Dhriti, is the best striker.

> The girl, who is in charge of training Dhriti, is our best striker.

Dhriti is in charge of training, and she's the best striker.

> The girl who is in charge of training, Dhriti, is our best striker.

Add commas to the sentences to match the meanings in bold.

1 **Frank and Emily built a den after they woke Alyssa up.**

After waking up Alyssa Frank and Emily built a den.

2 **Alyssa, Frank and Emily built a den after they woke up.**

After waking up Alyssa Frank and Emily built a den.

Explain the difference in meaning between the two sentences below.

1 The children, who had run into the castle, immediately came out again.

....

....

2 The children, who had run into the castle immediately, came out again.

....

....

13

Relative Clauses

A relative clause is a type of subordinate clause. It gives extra information about a noun.

relative clause

The mouse **who was at war with the cat** waited for battle.

Relative clauses can be introduced by **relative pronouns**, such as **that**, **which**, **who** and **whose**. The words **where** and **when** can also introduce a relative clause.

Sometimes, the relative pronoun can be left out, and the sentence will still make sense.

The relative clause 'I found at the beach' could be introduced by 'that'.

The stone **I found at the beach** looked like an egg.

Match each main clause with the correct relative clause.

I gave a night light to my sister Annie — who doesn't like the dark.

The class was intrigued by the box — the teacher brought in.

We went down to the river — where we saw the crocodile.

Tom remembered to feed the cat — which hissed at him.

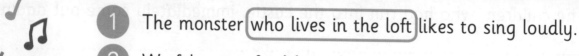

Circle the relative clause in each of the sentences below.

1. The monster who lives in the loft likes to sing loudly.
2. We felt sorry for Max whose team was losing.
3. The sundae I bought with my pocket money was lovely.
4. We bought chips at the beach which had a rock pool.
5. We found Ben, who had been hiding, so we went home.

Write a suitable word in the gaps below, then circle the relative clause in each sentence.

1. My brother, ... is very good at ballet, goes to a dancing school.

2. The man .... dog had a sweet tooth had to buy another cake.

3. I didn't want to cross the field .... the cows were grazing.

4. Joyce had chicken and chips .... is her favourite meal.

5. I didn't enjoy watching the film .... my brother had chosen.

6. My friends met up at the park .... is close to my house.

Add your own relative clause to each sentence below.

1. The sandcastle _which had turrets and a moat_ has been washed away.

2. I went on holiday with my stepsister Lily ....

3. My aunty, ..., is going to Greece.

4. After lunch, we walked to the shop ....

5. The scary house .... has burned down.

Underline all the relative clauses in the passage.

Sven, who liked to go ice-fishing, set off for the frozen lakes which were in the mountains near his village. When he got to the lake where he normally fished, there were lots of people skating on it, so Sven decided to go to another lake which was quieter. He reached the lake, and as he fished, he heard a tapping sound. A few seconds later, a cow whose horns were purple popped out of the ice next to Sven.

Linking Ideas

Adverbs and adverbial phrases tell you how, when, where or how often something happens. They also help to link ideas together.

Firstly, I'm going to the cinema. I'm having tea **after that**.

 This is called cohesion.

These adverbials help the two sentences to flow together by telling you how the events are linked.

Fill in the gaps below with the correct adverbial phrase.

in the kitchen   ~~on the first day~~   at the lake

on Wednesday   on the following day

Monday	Tuesday	Wednesday	Thursday	Friday
snorkelling	climbing	fun park	sailing	baking

When I went to summer camp, I went snorkelling on the first day. The

activity .... was just as fun — I climbed a giant tree.

We all went to a fun park .... Thursday's activity was

a boat race .... Finally, we baked cookies ....

Rewrite the passage using the adverbials in the box.

then   later   in the dining room   firstly

Today, I started a new job. My boss showed me around.
He took me to my desk and gave me some work. I went to
have lunch and found that my boss had started a disco!

....

....

....

....

Practise and Learn

English
Ages 9-10

Answers

This section shows each of the pages from the book with the answers filled out.

The pages are laid out in the same way as the book itself, so the questions can be easily marked by you, or by your child.

There are also helpful learning tips with some of the pages.

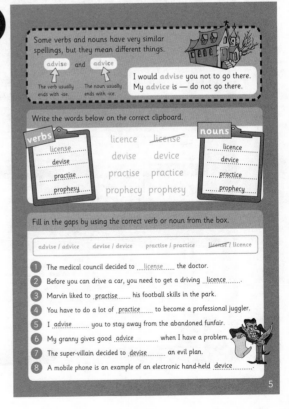

4 — **Commonly Confused Words**

Homophones are words that are pronounced the same, but have scent and sent different spellings and meanings.

Fill in the homophones and then find all the words in the wordsearch.

steal	⇒	S T E E L
herd	⇒	H E A R D
guessed	⇒	G U E S T
altar	⇒	A L T E R
aisle	⇒	I S L E

Write a sentence using each of these words.

VARIOUS ANSWERS POSSIBLE

past ⇒ I walk past the ...

passed ⇒ Jenny passed her exams.

allowed ⇒ I'm not allowed to eat sweets before dinner.

aloud ⇒ My dad sometimes sings aloud in the shower.

Find homophones for each of the words below.

led	⇒	L E A D	prophet	⇒	P R O F I T
serial	⇒	C E R E A L	draft	⇒	D R A U G H T
farther	⇒	F A T H E R	mourning	⇒	M O R N I N G

4

Reading these words aloud might help your child to think of homophones.

5

Some verbs and nouns have very similar spellings, but they mean different things.

advise and advice

The verb usually ends with -ise. The noun usually ends with -ice.

I would **advise** you not to go there. My **advice** is — do not go there.

Write the words below on the correct clipboard.

verbs: license, devise, practise, prophesy

licence ~~license~~ devise device practise practice prophecy prophesy

nouns: licence, device, practice, prophecy

Fill in the gaps by using the correct verb or noun from the box.

advise / advice   devise / device   practise / practice   licence / licence

1. The medical council decided to __license__ the doctor.
2. Before you can drive a car, you need to get a driving __licence__.
3. Marvin liked to __practise__ his football skills in the park.
4. You have to do a lot of __practice__ to become a professional juggler.
5. I __advise__ you to stay away from the abandoned funfair.
6. My granny gives good __advice__ when I have a problem.
7. The super-villain decided to __devise__ an evil plan.
8. A mobile phone is an example of an electronic hand-held __device__.

5

6

Word Endings

Sometimes words sound similar, but are spelled differently.

incredible and vegetable   horribly and tolerably

Words ending in -ible and -able sound similar.   Words ending in -ibly and -ably also sound similar.

Cross out the bold word in each sentence below that is spelled incorrectly.

1. Arnold finally achieved the ~~impossable~~ / **impossible** and caught his tail.
2. Eve's slice of cake was **considerably** / ~~consideribly~~ larger than Anna's.
3. The bike my parents bought for me has an ~~adjustible~~ / **adjustable** seat.
4. My brother was **visibly** / ~~visably~~ scared of my tarantula.
5. The boy crossed the road **sensibly** / ~~sensably~~ on the way to school.
6. The island is only ~~accessable~~ / **accessible** on foot when the tide is low.

Finish the words in the sentences using **-able**, **-ible**, **-ably** or **-ibly**.

1. The hamsters were so ador **able** that we bought three.
2. My dad told me it was irrespons **ible** to lie to my brother.
3. Faruq won the cycling race comfort **ably**.
4. When I write quickly, my writing is illeg **ible**.
5. Mrs Burrows, my piano teacher, is very depend **able**.
6. The friar was terr **ibly** pleased when the rain stopped.
7. It was debat **able** whether the outlaw was a hero.

6

7

The endings **-ant** and **-ent** both sound like 'unt'. → participant   frequent

resistance   obedience ← The endings **-ance** and **-ence** both sound like 'unce'.

The endings **-ancy** and **-ency** both sound like 'uncy'. → hesitancy   emergency

The endings **-ent**, **-ence** and **-ency** usually come after **soft 'c'** sounds, **soft 'g'** sounds and **'qu'**, but there are lots of exceptions.

Add **-ant** or **-ent** to the words below to spell them correctly. Write the completed words on the correct clipboard.

delinqu...   obedi...
observ...   independ...
toler...   expect...
innoc...   assist...

ent
delinquent
innocent
obedient
independent

ant
observant
tolerant
expectant
assistant

Choose the correct ending to complete the sentences.

| ance | ence | ancy | ency |

1. She had the dec**ency** to apologise for taking my pen without asking.
2. He helped an elderly man who needed assist**ance** crossing the road.
3. Zara felt full of confid**ence** the night before her swimming gala.
4. The restaurant had a job vac**ancy** for a new chef.
5. The thief pleaded his innoc**ence** to the judge.
6. The mysterious subst**ance** could only be one thing — alien goo!
7. "Don't adjust the radio frequ**ency**!" warned the police chief.

7

If your child finds this page tricky, encourage them to look up the words in a dictionary.

8

Changing Word Types

You can add a suffix to the end of a word to make nouns or adjectives into verbs. You sometimes have to change the spelling of the root word.

Noun to **Verb**   **Adjective** to **Verb**
liquid ⇨ liquidise   active ⇨ activate

Adding **-ise**, **-ify** and **-en** can turn nouns into verbs. Add the correct suffix to the nouns below, and sort the new words into the right box.

~~fright~~	horror	quiet	glory	advert
class	strength	summary	memory	

en	ise	ify
frighten	advertise	horrify
quieten	summarise	glorify
strengthen	memorise	classify

Choose the correct suffix to make the adjectives below into verbs.

| ify | ate | ise | en |

Using step-by-step instructions can _simplify_ a difficult task. ⇨ simple
Madha performed a silly dance to _lighten_ the mood. ⇨ light
Abe didn't _hesitate_ before stepping out onto the stage. ⇨ hesitant
I let the jelly _solidify_ before serving it. ⇨ solid
Moe and Joe _specialise_ in digging tunnels. ⇨ special
First, _soften_ the butter in a saucepan. ⇨ soft

8

9

Prefixes

A prefix can be added to the start of a word to change its meaning.

un + graceful = ungraceful   dis + graceful = disgraceful

Even though both words have the root word 'graceful', adding a prefix changes the meaning.

Add either **re-** or **mis-** to complete the sentences below and match the meaning in brackets.

1. Jack _mis_placed his phone. (Jack lost his phone.)
2. Jack _re_placed his phone. (Jack bought a new phone.)
3. Tim _mis_read the instructions. (Tim read the instructions wrongly.)
4. Tim _re_read the instructions. (Tim read the instructions again.)

One sentence below uses the prefix **dis-**, the other uses the prefix **re-**. Explain the difference in meaning between the two sentences.

1. The mayor was disappointed after the council's decision.
   This sentence means that the mayor felt upset.
2. The mayor was reappointed after the council's decision.
   This sentence means that the mayor was made mayor again.

Write a sentence ~~using~~ words on the left.

VARIOUS ANSWERS POSSIBLE

...like most vegetables.
unlike ⇨ Barbara's sprout jam is unlike anything I've ever tasted.
devalued ⇨ The leaking roof devalued the house.
undervalued ⇨ The antiques expert undervalued the diamond ring.

9

You could also ask pupils to explain the difference between 'unable' and 'disable'; 'discover' and 'recover'; 'uncover' and 'undercover'.

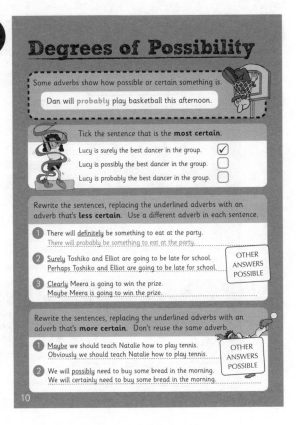

10 — Degrees of Possibility

Some adverbs show how possible or certain something is.

Dan will **probably** play basketball this afternoon.

Tick the sentence that is the **most certain**.

Lucy is surely the best dancer in the group. ✓
Lucy is possibly the best dancer in the group. ☐
Lucy is probably the best dancer in the group. ☐

Rewrite the sentences, replacing the underlined adverbs with an adverb that's **less certain**. Use a different adverb in each sentence.

1 There will <u>definitely</u> be something to eat at the party.
There will probably be something to eat at the party.

2 <u>Surely</u> Toshiko and Elliot are going to be late for school.
Perhaps Toshiko and Elliot are going to be late for school.

3 <u>Clearly</u> Meera is going to win the prize.
Maybe Meera is going to win the prize.

OTHER ANSWERS POSSIBLE

Rewrite the sentences, replacing the underlined adverbs with an adverb that's **more certain**. Don't reuse the same adverb.

1 <u>Maybe</u> we should teach Natalie how to play tennis.
Obviously we should teach Natalie how to play tennis.

2 We will <u>possibly</u> need to buy some bread in the morning.
We will certainly need to buy some bread in the morning.

OTHER ANSWERS POSSIBLE

10

11

Modal verbs also show how certain or possible something is. They're used to give more information about the main verb in a sentence.

I **will** go to the beach. (modal verb / main verb)

I **might** go to the beach. ('might' shows that going to the beach is possible, but not certain.)

Circle the modal verb in each of the sentences below.

1 We (may) go to the park.
2 You (could) try the library.
3 He (can) meet you tomorrow.
4 I (might) be late.
5 Peter (will) help you find the bag.
6 After my swim, I (shall) eat lunch.
7 Sue (should) be here by now.
8 You (must) not run in the classroom.

Tick the sentence that is **the most certain**.

Anya might take the shoes back to the shop tomorrow. ☐
Anya shall take the shoes back to the shop tomorrow. ✓
Anya may take the shoes back to the shop tomorrow. ☐
Anya should take the shoes back to the shop tomorrow. ☐

Circle the modal verb in each sentence which is **less certain**.

1 Josiah (might) / must ride his bike tomorrow.
2 We will / (could) go and visit our grandma.
3 I can / (may) take the dog for a walk.
4 I (should) / must tidy my room tonight.
5 The brave princess says she shall / (could) fight the terrible dragon.

11

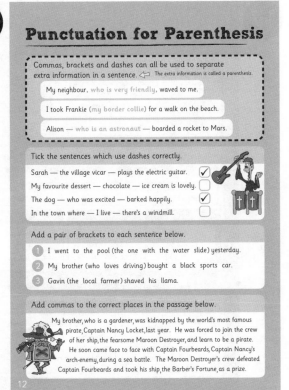

12 — Punctuation for Parenthesis

Commas, brackets and dashes can all be used to separate extra information in a sentence. ⇐ *The extra information is called a parenthesis.*

My neighbour, who is very friendly, waved to me.

I took Frankie (my border collie) for a walk on the beach.

Alison — who is an astronaut — boarded a rocket to Mars.

Tick the sentences which use dashes correctly.

Sarah — the village vicar — plays the electric guitar. ✓
My favourite dessert — chocolate — ice cream is lovely. ☐
The dog — who was excited — barked happily. ✓
In the town where — I live — there's a windmill. ☐

Add a pair of brackets to each sentence below.

1 I went to the pool (the one with the water slide) yesterday.
2 My brother (who loves driving) bought a black sports car.
3 Gavin (the local farmer) shaved his llama.

Add commas to the correct places in the passage below.

My brother, who is a gardener, was kidnapped by the world's most famous pirate, Captain Nancy Locket, last year. He was forced to join the crew of her ship, the fearsome Maroon Destroyer, and learn to be a pirate. He soon came face to face with Captain Fourbeards, Captain Nancy's arch-enemy, during a sea battle. The Maroon Destroyer's crew defeated Captain Fourbeards and took his ship, the Barber's Fortune, as a prize.

12

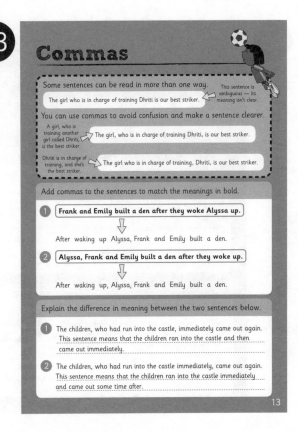

13 — Commas

Some sentences can be read in more than one way. *This sentence is ambiguous — its meaning isn't clear.*

The girl who is in charge of training Dhriti is our best striker.

You can use commas to avoid confusion and make a sentence clearer.

A girl, who is training another girl called Dhriti, is the best striker.
The girl, who is in charge of training Dhriti, is our best striker.

Dhriti is in charge of training, and she's the best striker.
The girl who is in charge of training, Dhriti, is our best striker.

Add commas to the sentences to match the meanings in bold.

1 **Frank and Emily built a den after they woke Alyssa up.**
⬇
After waking up Alyssa, Frank and Emily built a den.

2 **Alyssa, Frank and Emily built a den after they woke up.**
⬇
After waking up, Alyssa, Frank and Emily built a den.

Explain the difference in meaning between the two sentences below.

1 The children, who had run into the castle, immediately came out again.
This sentence means that the children ran into the castle and then came out immediately.

2 The children, who had run into the castle immediately, came out again.
This sentence means that the children ran into the castle immediately and came out some time after.

13

Ask pupils to find examples of punctuation for parenthesis in some books that they are reading.

14 Relative Clauses

A relative clause is a type of subordinate clause. It gives extra information about a noun.

relative clause

The mouse **who was at war with the cat** waited for battle.

Relative clauses can be introduced by **relative pronouns**, such as **that**, **which**, **who** and **whose**. The words **where** and **when** can also introduce a relative clause.

Sometimes, the relative pronoun can be left out, and the sentence will still make sense.

The relative clause 'I found at the beach' could be introduced by 'that'.

The stone **I found at the beach** looked like an egg.

Match each main clause with the correct relative clause.

- I gave a night light to my sister Annie — who doesn't like the dark.
- The class was intrigued by the box — the teacher brought in.
- We went down to the river — where we saw the crocodile.
- Tom remembered to feed the cat — which hissed at him.

Circle the relative clause in each of the sentences below.

1. The monster **who lives in the loft** likes to sing loudly.
2. We felt sorry for Max **whose team was losing**.
3. The sundae **I bought with my pocket money** was lovely.
4. We bought chips at the beach **which had a rock pool**.
5. We found Ben, **who had been hiding**, so we went home.

14

Remind pupils that although a lot of questions start with 'who', 'where', 'when' etc, they are not examples of relative clauses.

15

Write a suitable word in the gaps below, then circle the relative clause in each sentence.

OTHER ANSWERS POSSIBLE

1. My brother, **who is very good at ballet** goes to a dancing
2. The man **whose dog had a sweet tooth** had to buy another cake.
3. I didn't want to cross the field **where the cows were grazing**.
4. Joyce had chicken and chips **which is her favourite meal**.
5. I didn't enjoy watching the film **that my brother had chosen**.
6. My friends met up at the park **which is close to my house**.

Add your own relative clause to each sentence below.

OTHER ANSWERS POSSIBLE

1. The sandcastle **which had turrets and a moat** has been...
2. I went on holiday with my stepsister Lily **who has long red hair**.
3. My aunty, **whose dog is called Bernie**, is going to Greece.
4. After lunch, we walked to the shop **which sells ice cream**.
5. The scary house **that had been abandoned** has burned down.

Underline all the relative clauses in the passage.

Sven, **who liked to go ice-fishing**, set off for the frozen lakes **which were in the mountains near his village**. When he got to the lake **where he normally fished**, there were lots of people skating on it, so Sven decided to go to another lake **which was quieter**. He reached the lake, and as he fished, he heard a tapping sound. A few seconds later, a cow **whose horns were purple** popped out of the ice next to Sven.

15

16 Linking Ideas

Adverbs and adverbial phrases tell you how, when, where or how often something happens. They also help to link ideas together.

Firstly, I'm going to the cinema. I'm having tea **after that**.

These adverbials help the two sentences to flow together by telling you how the events are linked.

This is called cohesion.

Fill in the gaps below with the correct adverbial phrase.

| in the kitchen | on the first day | at the lake |
| on Wednesday | | on the following day |

Monday	Tuesday	Wednesday	Thursday	Friday
snorkelling	climbing	fun park	sailing	baking

When I went to summer camp, I went snorkelling **on the first day**. The activity **on the following day** was just as fun — I climbed a giant tree. We all went to a fun park **on Wednesday**. Thursday's activity was a boat race **at the lake**. Finally, we baked cookies **in the kitchen**.

Rewrite the passage using the adverbials in the box.

| then | later | in the dining room | firstly |

Today, I started a new job. My boss showed me around. He took me to my desk and gave me some work. I went to have lunch and found that my boss had started a disco!

Today, I started a new job. **Firstly**, my boss showed me around. **Then** he took me to my desk and gave me some work. **Later**, I went to have lunch **in the dining room** and found that my boss had started a disco!

16

17

You can also use adverbial phrases to show how paragraphs are related — this helps to link them together smoothly. Adverbials can show place, time or number.

The first paragraph is introduced by an adverbial of time that shows when the holiday happened.

Last week, my family went on holiday in Cornwall. We stayed in a caravan next to the beach.

At the beach, there was a surfing school where my brother and I had lessons each morning.

An adverbial of place is used to show the second paragraph is linked to the beach that was mentioned in the first paragraph.

Put each adverbial below into the correct box to show whether it could link paragraphs by place, time or number.

| in the station | at 9 am | before lunch | beside her | finally |
| after band practice | secondly | at the park | for the fifth time |

place	time	number
in the station	at 9 am	finally
beside her	before lunch	secondly
at the park	after band practice	for the fifth time

Write a suitable adverbial in each gap to link the paragraphs.

In the morning, the **OTHER ANSWERS POSSIBLE** was getting ready the moon. It took

Finally, she was ready to board the rocket, which would soon be launched into space.

Last night, we set off on holiday. We were in the car when we realised that our dog was missing.

Back home, the dog was hiding so that he didn't have to come with us — he doesn't like the car.

17

Traditional Stories

Traditional stories have been passed down and retold for hundreds of years. Read this traditional story about King Arthur.

The Sword in the Stone

Ancient Britain was ruled by King Uther, and he had a son named Arthur. Merlin, the court's wizard, was worried that Arthur might be in danger because the monarchy had so many enemies. Uther and Merlin decided that the only way to make sure Arthur was safe was to raise him in secret so that nobody would know that he was the king's son.

When King Uther died, all of his enemies claimed that they should be the next king of Britain. Merlin told the men that he would use magic to decide who should be the next king. Using his wizardry, Merlin put a magical sword called Excalibur into an enormous anvil on a stone. On the side of the stone Merlin wrote, 'Whoever pulls this sword out of this stone and anvil is the rightful king, born to rule England.'

Many strong and brave knights tried to pull the sword out of the stone, but none of them succeeded. Arthur asked if he could try, but all the knights laughed at him because he looked so small and weak. However, as soon as he tried to pull out Excalibur, the sword slid out. Once they realised that Arthur was the true king of Britain, the knights quickly stopped laughing.

18

Reread the story and answer these questions in full sentences.

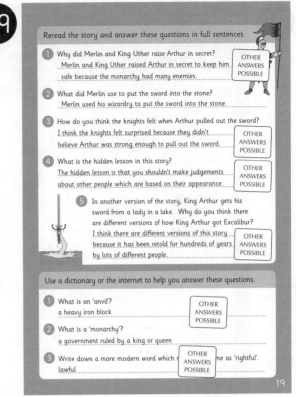

1. Why did Merlin and King Uther raise Arthur in secret?
Merlin and King Uther raised Arthur in secret to keep him safe because the monarchy had many enemies.

2. What did Merlin use to put the sword into the stone?
Merlin used his wizardry to put the sword into the stone.

3. How do you think the knights felt when Arthur pulled out the sword? **OTHER ANSWERS POSSIBLE**
I think the knights felt surprised because they didn't believe Arthur was strong enough to pull out the sword.

4. What is the hidden lesson in this story? **OTHER ANSWERS POSSIBLE**
The hidden lesson is that you shouldn't make judgements about other people which are based on their appearance.

5. In another version of the story, King Arthur gets his sword from a lady in a lake. Why do you think there are different versions of how King Arthur got Excalibur? **OTHER ANSWERS POSSIBLE**
I think there are different versions of this story because it has been retold for hundreds of years by lots of different people.

Use a dictionary or the internet to help you answer these questions.

1. What is an 'anvil'? **OTHER ANSWERS POSSIBLE**
a heavy iron block

2. What is a 'monarchy'?
a government ruled by a king or queen

3. Write down a more modern word which means the same as 'rightful'. **OTHER ANSWERS POSSIBLE**
lawful

19

It might be helpful to discuss the story with your child before they tackle the more difficult questions.

Fables

Fables are stories that have a moral. A moral is a lesson that is hidden in a story. Read this short Chinese fable about a cracked pot.

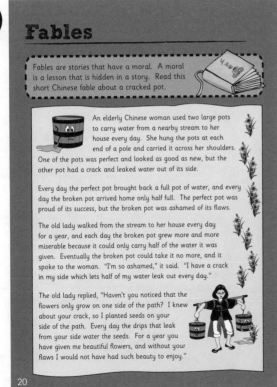

An elderly Chinese woman used two large pots to carry water from a nearby stream to her house every day. She hung the pots at each end of a pole and carried it across her shoulders. One of the pots was perfect and looked as good as new, but the other pot had a crack and leaked water out of its side.

Every day the perfect pot brought back a full pot of water, and every day the broken pot arrived home only half full. The perfect pot was proud of its success, but the broken pot was ashamed of its flaws.

The old lady walked from the stream to her house every day for a year, and each day the broken pot grew more and more miserable because it could only carry half of the water it was given. Eventually the broken pot could take it no more, and it spoke to the woman. "I'm so ashamed," it said. "I have a crack in my side which lets half of my water leak out every day."

The old lady replied, "Haven't you noticed that the flowers only grow on one side of the path? I knew about your crack, so I planted seeds on your side of the path. Every day the drips that leak from your side water the seeds. For a year you have given me beautiful flowers, and without your flaws I would not have had such beauty to enjoy."

20

Reread the fable and answer these questions in full sentences.

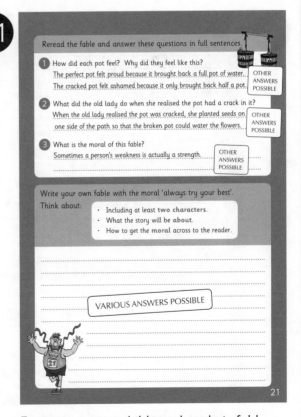

1. How did each pot feel? Why did they feel like this? **OTHER ANSWERS POSSIBLE**
The perfect pot felt proud because it brought back a full pot of water. The cracked pot felt ashamed because it only brought back half a pot.

2. What did the old lady do when she realised the pot had a crack in it? **OTHER ANSWERS POSSIBLE**
When the old lady realised the pot was cracked, she planted seeds on one side of the path so that the broken pot could water the flowers.

3. What is the moral of this fable? **OTHER ANSWERS POSSIBLE**
Sometimes a person's weakness is actually a strength.

Write your own fable with the moral 'always try your best'.
Think about:
- Including at least **two characters**.
- What the story will be **about**.
- How to get the **moral** across to the reader.

VARIOUS ANSWERS POSSIBLE

21

Encourage your child to plan their fable on a piece of rough paper using the suggestions in the white box. Then get them to write it out on the page.

22

Understanding Poetry

Poetry can tell stories and create different moods. Read this poem aloud and then answer the questions on the next page.

The Sleepy Giant

My age is three hundred and seventy-two,
And I think, with the deepest regret,
How I used to pick up and voraciously chew
The dear little boys whom I met.

I've eaten them raw, in their holiday suits;
I've eaten them curried with rice;
I've eaten them baked, in their jackets and boots,
And found them exceedingly nice.

But now that my jaws are too weak for such fare,
I think it exceedingly rude
To do such a thing, when I'm quite well aware
Little boys do not like to be chewed.

And so I contentedly live upon eels,
And try to do nothing amiss,
And I pass all the time I can spare from my meals
In innocent slumber — like this.

by Charles E. Carryl

23

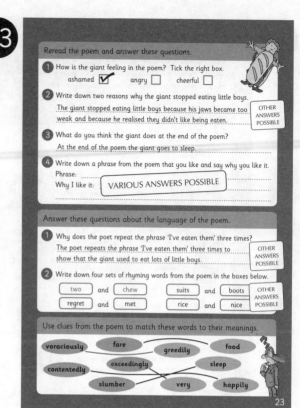

Reread the poem and answer these questions.

1. How is the giant feeling in the poem? Tick the right box.
   ashamed ☑   angry ☐   cheerful ☐

2. Write down two reasons why the giant stopped eating little boys.
   The giant stopped eating little boys because his jaws became too weak and because he realised they didn't like being eaten.
   OTHER ANSWERS POSSIBLE

3. What do you think the giant does at the end of the poem?
   At the end of the poem the giant goes to sleep.

4. Write down a phrase from the poem that you like and say why you like it.
   Phrase:
   Why I like it: VARIOUS ANSWERS POSSIBLE

Answer these questions about the language of the poem.

1. Why does the poet repeat the phrase 'I've eaten them' three times?
   The poet repeats the phrase 'I've eaten them' three times to show that the giant used to eat lots of little boys.
   OTHER ANSWERS POSSIBLE

2. Write down four sets of rhyming words from the poem in the boxes below.
   two and chew   suits and boots
   regret and met   rice and nice
   OTHER ANSWERS POSSIBLE

Use clues from the poem to match these words to their meanings.

voraciously — fare — greedily — food
contentedly — exceedingly — sleep
slumber — very — happily

Using clues in a text to work out the meaning of a word is a useful skill, so encourage your child to try the third exercise without a dictionary.

24

Informative Writing

Informative writing is text which is mostly made up of facts.

The SWAMP!

The UK's first swamp-themed Theme Park!

The **SWAMP** has plenty of rides to keep the whole family entertained! There's a HUGE roller coaster, as well as a log flume for those who don't mind getting wet! For our younger visitors, there's also the teacups and a carousel.

Brand new
SWAMP TUNNEL
A gentle family ride with guaranteed gunk!

The **SWAMP** is home to the SWAMP CREW: Slimy Sid, Gungy Godfrey and Gooey Gertie. These cuddly characters are here to make your visit
SWAMPTACULAR!

We also have an arcade and fairground games — there's something for kids of all ages!

Don't forget to buy tickets to see our latest **ballet** — Swamp Lake.

The **SWAMP** is home to the **only** Gunge Pool restaurant in the UK. With a range of meals to choose from, it's sure to hit the spot:
- Slime Burgers
- Gooey Fries
- Fried Fungi
- Gunged Potatoes
- Slippery Spaghetti
- Gloopy Sausages

Please get in touch — we'd love to hear from you!
✉ info@theswamp.com
☎ 09099 565687

Read the leaflet and then answer the questions below.

1. Write down four of the rides that are mentioned in the leaflet.
   1. roller coaster   3. teacups
   2. log flume   4. carousel
   OTHER ANSWERS POSSIBLE

2. What are the two ways of contacting The Swamp?
   1. email   2. telephone

3. How do you know that The Swamp is suitable for young children?
   Because there are rides for "younger visitors" and the arcade and fairground games are "for kids of all ages".
   OTHER ANSWERS POSSIBLE

As an extension, your child could design an informative leaflet about their own theme park. Encourage them to use colour and images to make it look appealing.

25

Lists and Summaries

Summaries are shorter versions of long bits of writing. Summaries and lists are useful because they make it easier to remember the important points in longer bits of text.

Read this passage about planning parties.

Organising a party can be quite scary. A lot of people worry that the food will go wrong, or their guests will get bored, or that no one will come in the first place. The key to stress-free party-planning is to be prepared for disasters.

Even if you're having fancy party food, keep an emergency supply of crisps, sandwiches and biscuits. These are perfect because they come in loads of different flavours, so there will be something to please all your guests. Similarly, have a choice of films to watch, in case your guests get tired of games, dancing and chatting.

Finally, write your contact details on your invitations and ask people to tell you if they can or can't come. Then you'll know exactly who's coming, so you can be fully prepared.

List three ways to prepare for party disasters.

1. Keep an emergency supply of crisps, sandwiches and biscuits.
2. Have a choice of films to watch.
3. Write your contact details on your invitations.

Summarise the main points from the text in fewer than 50 words.

VARIOUS ANSWERS POSSIBLE

Adverts

Adverts are usually a mix of informative writing (giving lots of facts) and persuasive writing (trying to persuade you to do something).

Read these adverts from a local newspaper.

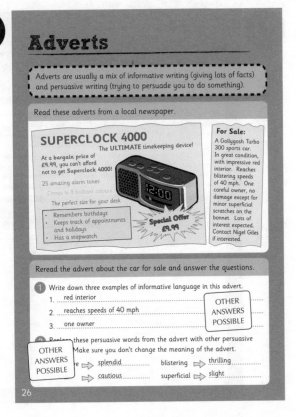

SUPERCLOCK 4000
The **ULTIMATE** timekeeping device!

At a bargain price of £9.99, you can't afford not to get Superclock 4000!

25 amazing alarm tones

Comes in 5 brilliant colours

The perfect size for your desk

- Remembers birthdays
- Keeps track of appointments and holidays
- Has a stopwatch

Special Offer £9.99

For Sale:
A Gollygosh Turbo 300 sports car. In great condition, with impressive red interior. Reaches blistering speeds of 40 mph. One careful owner, no damage except for minor superficial scratches on the bonnet. Lots of interest expected. Contact Nigel Giles if interested.

Reread the advert about the car for sale and answer the questions.

1. Write down three examples of informative language in this advert.
   1. red interior
   2. reaches speeds of 40 mph   *OTHER ANSWERS POSSIBLE*
   3. one owner

2. Replace these persuasive words from the advert with other persuasive... Make sure you don't change the meaning of the advert.   *OTHER ANSWERS POSSIBLE*

   ... ⇒ splendid   blistering ⇒ thrilling

   ⇒ cautious   superficial ⇒ slight

Reread the Superclock 4000 advert and then answer these questions.

1. Write down two reasons why a customer might buy the clock.
   1. ....
   2. ....   *VARIOUS ANSWERS POSSIBLE*

2. Write down four adjectives from the advert.   *OTHER ANSWERS POSSIBLE*
   1. ultimate   2. amazing
   3. perfect   4. brilliant

3. Rewrite the Superclock 4000 advert using full sentences. Add some more adjectives to make it more interesting.

   The incredible, new SUPERCLOCK 4000 is the ultimate timekeeping device.

   VARIOUS ANSWERS POSSIBLE

Write your own advert in the space below. Make sure you use lots of adjectives which will persuade someone to buy your product.

Product name

Description or slogan

Bullet points about product   *VARIOUS ANSWERS POSSIBLE*

Price

...rmation

As an extension, your child could design a poster advertising something they love. Explain that it should be visually appealing as well as informative and persuasive.

Newspaper Reports

Newspaper reports are full of facts, opinions and persuasive language. Read this report about the problem of littering.

Littering Isn't Just Trash Talk

The town of Ulverbury is faced with a very real problem. The state of the streets is getting worse and worse, as littering and dog fouling increase steadily. One local resident, Jerome Pollitzer, 51, has decided to take the problem into his own hands.

"I've written countless letters to the council, and had no response," he told me. "It's absolutely ridiculous that they haven't done anything about it."

Looking at the streets of Ulverbury, Mr Pollitzer has a point. The pavements are disgusting, and there's litter, dog muck and chewing gum everywhere. As tax-paying citizens, clean streets are the very least we should expect from the council, and they can't even do that right.

Mr Pollitzer has recently launched his own scheme called 'Trash Talk'. The 'Trash Talk' scheme involves handing out information leaflets and trying to get local residents to sign a petition asking the council to take littering more seriously. Mr Pollitzer also has some suggestions for solving the littering problem.

His suggestions include on-the-spot fines for people caught red-handed and also giving litterbugs a taste of their own medicine, by making them do community service picking up rubbish. He's also keen to set up a special phone line so that people can report 'criminals' anonymously. I, for one, hope Mr Pollitzer is successful, because litter makes Ulverbury look terrible.

by **Ian Desine**

Answer the questions below about the newspaper report.

1. Write down three persuasive words in the report which grab your attention.
   ridiculous, disgusting, terrible   *OTHER ANSWERS POSSIBLE*

2. How do you think Mr Pollitzer was feeling when he was interviewed?
   frustrated   *VARIOUS ANSWERS POSSIBLE*

3. List the three possible solutions that Mr Pollitzer wants to try.
   1. On-the-spot fines for people caught red-handed.
   2. Making litterbugs do community service picking up rubbish.
   3. Setting up a special phone line so people can report 'criminals'.

Imagine that you are a reporter investigating a spaceship that has landed in your local area. Think up answers to the questions below.

1. Where have the aliens landed? When did they arrive?

2. What are the aliens called? What do they look like?

3. What do the...   *VARIOUS ANSWERS POSSIBLE*

4. What do the local residents think about the aliens' arrival?

Use your answers above to write a newspaper report about the alien landing. Write your headline in the grey box and draw a picture.

VARIOUS ANSWERS POSSIBLE

Write your name here. ⇒ By

Encourage your child to read some articles in a newspaper or on a news website and to write in a similar style.

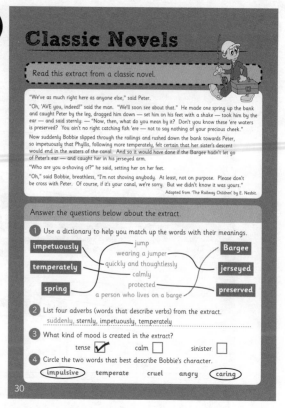

30 Classic Novels

Read this extract from a classic novel.

"We've as much right here as anyone else," said Peter.

"Oh, 'AVE you, indeed!" said the man. "We'll soon see about that." He made one spring up the bank and caught Peter by the leg, dragged him down — set him on his feet with a shake — took him by the ear — and said sternly: — "Now, then, what do you mean by it? Don't you know these 'ere waters is preserved? You ain't no right catching fish 'ere — not to say nothing of your precious cheek."

Now suddenly Bobbie slipped through the railings and rushed down the bank towards Peter, so impetuously that Phyllis, following more temperately, felt certain that her sister's descent would end in the waters of the canal. And so it would have done if the Bargee hadn't let go of Peter's ear — and caught her in his jerseyed arm.

"Who are you a-shoving of?" he said, setting her on her feet.

"Oh," said Bobbie, breathless, "I'm not shoving anybody. At least, not on purpose. Please don't be cross with Peter. Of course, if it's your canal, we're sorry. But we didn't know it was yours."

Adapted from 'The Railway Children' by E. Nesbit.

Answer the questions below about the extract.

1 Use a dictionary to help you match up the words with their meanings.

- **impetuously** — quickly and thoughtlessly
- **temperately** — calmly
- **spring** — jump
- **Bargee** — a person who lives on a barge
- **jerseyed** — wearing a jumper
- **preserved** — protected

2 List four adverbs (words that describe verbs) from the extract.
suddenly, sternly, impetuously, temperately

3 What kind of mood is created in the extract?
tense ✓   calm ☐   sinister ☐

4 Circle the two words that best describe Bobbie's character.
(impulsive)   temperate   cruel   angry   (caring)

30

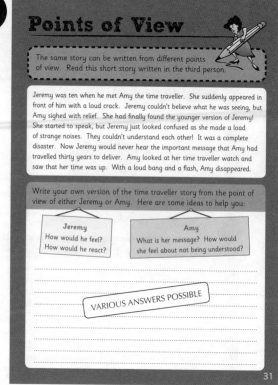

31 Points of View

The same story can be written from different points of view. Read this short story written in the third person.

Jeremy was ten when he met Amy the time traveller. She suddenly appeared in front of him with a loud crack. Jeremy couldn't believe what he was seeing, but Amy sighed with relief. She had finally found the younger version of Jeremy! She started to speak, but Jeremy just looked confused as she made a load of strange noises. They couldn't understand each other! It was a complete disaster. Now Jeremy would never hear the important message that Amy had travelled thirty years to deliver. Amy looked at her time traveller watch and saw that her time was up. With a loud bang and a flash, Amy disappeared.

Write your own version of the time traveller story from the point of view of either Jeremy or Amy. Here are some ideas to help you:

Jeremy
How would he feel?
How would he react?

Amy
What is her message? How would she feel about not being understood?

VARIOUS ANSWERS POSSIBLE

31

Before writing their own version, ask your child to imagine that they are their chosen character and discuss how they would feel in the same situation.

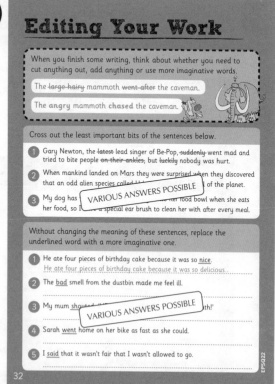

32 Editing Your Work

When you finish some writing, think about whether you need to cut anything out, add anything or use more imaginative words.

The ~~large hairy~~ mammoth ~~went after~~ the caveman.

The **angry** mammoth **chased** the caveman.

Cross out the least important bits of the sentences below.

1 Gary Newton, the ~~latest~~ lead singer of Be-Pop, ~~suddenly~~ went mad and tried to bite people ~~on their ankles~~, but ~~luckily~~ nobody was hurt.

2 When mankind landed on Mars they were surprised when they discovered that an odd alien species called ~~...~~ of the planet.

VARIOUS ANSWERS POSSIBLE

3 My dog has ~~...~~ her food bowl when she eats her food, so I ~~...~~ a special ear brush to clean her with after every meal.

Without changing the meaning of these sentences, replace the underlined word with a more imaginative one.

1 He ate four pieces of birthday cake because it was so _nice_.
He ate four pieces of birthday cake because it was so delicious.

2 The _bad_ smell from the dustbin made me feel ill.

3 My mum _shouted_ ~~...~~ th!'

VARIOUS ANSWERS POSSIBLE

4 Sarah _went_ home on her bike as fast as she could.

5 I _said_ that it wasn't fair that I wasn't allowed to go.

32

EP5Q22

Encourage your child to check every piece of work for mistakes, as well as editing it to make it sound better.

Race to the Island

You'll need a counter for each player and a dice. Place your counters at the start, and take it in turns to roll the dice once. Follow the instructions when you land on them.

START

cereal

noun

lengthen

possible answers include: may, might, will, should, could, can, must

sensible

possible answers include: that, which, who, whose

definitely

Something without an obvious meaning.

who is 42

FINISH

You can also use adverbial phrases to show how paragraphs are related — this helps to link them together smoothly. Adverbials can show place, time or number.

The first paragraph is introduced by an adverbial of time that shows when the holiday happened.

Last week, my family went on holiday in Cornwall. We stayed in a caravan next to the beach.

At the beach, there was a surfing school where my brother and I had lessons each morning.

An adverbial of place is used to show the second paragraph is linked to the beach that was mentioned in the first paragraph.

Put each adverbial below into the correct box to show whether it could link paragraphs by place, time or number.

~~in the station~~ at 9 am before lunch beside her finally
after band practice secondly at the park for the fifth time

place	time	number
in the station		

Write a suitable adverbial in each gap to link the paragraphs.

In the morning, the astronaut was getting ready to travel to the moon. It took many hours.

.................................., she was ready to board the rocket, which would soon be launched into space.

Last night, we set off on holiday. We were in the car when we realised that our dog was missing.

.........................., the dog was hiding so that he didn't have to come with us — he doesn't like the car.

17

Traditional Stories

Traditional stories have been passed down and retold for hundreds of years. Read this traditional story about King Arthur.

The Sword in the Stone

Ancient Britain was ruled by King Uther, and he had a son named Arthur. Merlin, the court's wizard, was worried that Arthur might be in danger because the monarchy had so many enemies. Uther and Merlin decided that the only way to make sure Arthur was safe was to raise him in secret so that nobody would know that he was the king's son.

When King Uther died, all of his enemies claimed that they should be the next king of Britain. Merlin told the men that he would use magic to decide who should be the next king. Using his wizardry, Merlin put a magical sword called Excalibur into an enormous anvil on a stone. On the side of the stone Merlin wrote, 'Whoever pulls this sword out of this stone and anvil is the rightful king, born to rule England.'

Many strong and brave knights tried to pull the sword out of the stone, but none of them succeeded. Arthur asked if he could try, but all the knights laughed at him because he looked so small and weak. However, as soon as he tried to pull out Excalibur, the sword slid out. Once they realised that Arthur was the true king of Britain, the knights quickly stopped laughing.

Reread the story and answer these questions in full sentences.

1 Why did Merlin and King Uther raise Arthur in secret?

....

....

2 What did Merlin use to put the sword into the stone?

....

3 How do you think the knights felt when Arthur pulled out the sword?

....

....

4 What is the hidden lesson in this story?

....

....

5 In another version of the story, King Arthur gets his sword from a lady in a lake. Why do you think there are different versions of how King Arthur got Excalibur?

....

....

....

Use a dictionary or the internet to help you answer these questions.

1 What is an 'anvil'?

....

2 What is a 'monarchy'?

....

3 Write down a more modern word which means the same as 'rightful'.

....

19

Fables

Fables are stories that have a moral. A moral is a lesson that is hidden in a story. Read this short Chinese fable about a cracked pot.

An elderly Chinese woman used two large pots to carry water from a nearby stream to her house every day. She hung the pots at each end of a pole and carried it across her shoulders. One of the pots was perfect and looked as good as new, but the other pot had a crack and leaked water out of its side.

Every day the perfect pot brought back a full pot of water, and every day the broken pot arrived home only half full. The perfect pot was proud of its success, but the broken pot was ashamed of its flaws.

The old lady walked from the stream to her house every day for a year, and each day the broken pot grew more and more miserable because it could only carry half of the water it was given. Eventually the broken pot could take it no more, and it spoke to the woman. "I'm so ashamed," it said. "I have a crack in my side which lets half of my water leak out every day."

The old lady replied, "Haven't you noticed that the flowers only grow on one side of the path? I knew about your crack, so I planted seeds on your side of the path. Every day the drips that leak from your side water the seeds. For a year you have given me beautiful flowers, and without your flaws I would not have had such beauty to enjoy."

Reread the fable and answer these questions in full sentences.

1 How did each pot feel? Why did they feel like this?

....

....

2 What did the old lady do when she realised the pot had a crack in it?

....

....

3 What is the moral of this fable?

....

....

Write your own fable with the moral 'always try your best'.

Think about:

- Including at least **two characters**.
- What the story will be **about**.
- How to get the **moral** across to the reader.

....

....

....

....

....

....

....

....

....

Understanding Poetry

Poetry can tell stories and create different moods. Read this poem aloud and then answer the questions on the next page.

The Sleepy Giant

My age is three hundred and seventy-two,
And I think, with the deepest regret,
How I used to pick up and voraciously chew
The dear little boys whom I met.

I've eaten them raw, in their holiday suits;
I've eaten them curried with rice;
I've eaten them baked, in their jackets and boots,
And found them exceedingly nice.

But now that my jaws are too weak for such fare,
I think it exceedingly rude
To do such a thing, when I'm quite well aware
Little boys do not like to be chewed.

And so I contentedly live upon eels,
And try to do nothing amiss,
And I pass all the time I can spare from my meals
In innocent slumber — like this.

by Charles E. Carryl

Reread the poem and answer these questions.

1 How is the giant feeling in the poem? Tick the right box.

ashamed ☐   angry ☐   cheerful ☐

2 Write down two reasons why the giant stopped eating little boys.

....

....

3 What do you think the giant does at the end of the poem?

....

4 Write down a phrase from the poem that you like and say why you like it.

Phrase: ....

Why I like it: ....

....

Answer these questions about the language of the poem.

1 Why does the poet repeat the phrase 'I've eaten them' three times?

....

....

2 Write down four sets of rhyming words from the poem in the boxes below.

| two | and | chew | | | and | |

| | and | | | | and | |

Use clues from the poem to match these words to their meanings.

voraciously   fare   greedily   food

exceedingly   sleep

contentedly

slumber   very   happily

23

Informative Writing

Informative writing is text which is mostly made up of facts.

The SWAMP!

The UK's first swamp-themed Theme Park!

The **SWAMP** has plenty of rides to keep the whole family entertained! There's a HUGE roller coaster, as well as a log flume for those who don't mind getting wet! For our younger visitors, there's also the teacups and a carousel.

Brand new

SWAMP TUNNEL
A gentle family ride with guaranteed gunk!

The **SWAMP** is home to the SWAMP CREW: **Slimy Sid**, **Gungy Godfrey** and **Gooey Gertie**. These cuddly characters are here to make your visit

SWAMPTACULAR!

We also have an arcade and fairground games — there's something for kids of all ages!

Don't forget to buy tickets to see our latest **ballet** — Swamp Lake.

The **SWAMP** is home to the **only** Gunge Pool restaurant in the UK. With a range of meals to choose from, it's sure to hit the spot:

- Slime Burgers
- Gooey Fries
- Fried Fungi
- Gunged Potatoes
- Slippery Spaghetti
- Gloopy Sausages

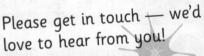

Please get in touch — we'd love to hear from you!

✉ info@theswamp.com
☎ 09099 565687

Read the leaflet and then answer the questions below.

1. Write down four of the rides that are mentioned in the leaflet.

   1. ....roller coaster.............................   3. ....

   2. ....   4. ....

2. What are the two ways of contacting The Swamp?

   1. ....   2. ....

3. How do you know that The Swamp is suitable for young children?

   ....

   ....

24

Lists and Summaries

Summaries are shorter versions of long bits of writing. Summaries and lists are useful because they make it easier to remember the important points in longer bits of text.

Read this passage about planning parties.

Organising a party can be quite scary. A lot of people worry that the food will go wrong, or their guests will get bored, or that no one will come in the first place. The key to stress-free party-planning is to be prepared for disasters.

Even if you're having fancy party food, keep an emergency supply of crisps, sandwiches and biscuits. These are perfect because they come in loads of different flavours, so there will be something to please all your guests. Similarly, have a choice of films to watch, in case your guests get tired of games, dancing and chatting.

Finally, write your contact details on your invitations and ask people to tell you if they can or can't come. Then you'll know exactly who's coming, so you can be fully prepared.

List three ways to prepare for party disasters.

1. ....

2. ....

3. ....

Summarise the main points from the text in fewer than 50 words.

....

....

....

....

....

25

Adverts

Read these adverts from a local newspaper.

SUPERCLOCK 4000

The **ULTIMATE** timekeeping device!

At a **bargain price** of **£9.99**, you can't afford not to get **Superclock 4000!**

25 amazing alarm tones

Comes in 5 brilliant colours

The perfect size for your desk

- Remembers birthdays
- Keeps track of appointments and holidays
- Has a stopwatch

Special Offer £9.99

For Sale:

A Gollygosh Turbo 300 sports car. In great condition, with impressive red interior. Reaches blistering speeds of 40 mph. One careful owner, no damage except for minor superficial scratches on the bonnet. Lots of interest expected. Contact Nigel Giles if interested.

Reread the advert about the car for sale and answer the questions.

1 Write down three examples of informative language in this advert.

1. ....

2. ....

3. ....

2 Replace these persuasive words from the advert with other persuasive words. Make sure you don't change the meaning of the advert.

impressive ⇨ ....   blistering ⇨ ....

careful ⇨ ....   superficial ⇨ ....

Reread the Superclock 4000 advert and then answer these questions.

1 Write down two reasons why a customer might buy the clock.

1. ....

2. ....

2 Write down four adjectives from the advert.

1. ....   2. ....

3. ....   4. ....

3 Rewrite the Superclock 4000 advert using full sentences.
Add some more adjectives to make it more interesting.

The incredible, new SUPERCLOCK 4000 is the ultimate timekeeping
device.
....
....
....
....

Write your own advert in the space below. Make sure you use lots of adjectives which will persuade someone to buy your product.

Product name ➘

Price ➘

Description or slogan ➘

Bullet points about product   Picture   More information

Newspaper Reports

Newspaper reports are full of facts, opinions and persuasive language. Read this report about the problem of littering.

Littering Isn't Just Trash Talk

The town of Ulverbury is faced with a very real problem. The state of the streets is getting worse and worse, as littering and dog fouling increase steadily. One local resident, Jerome Pollitzer, 51, has decided to take the problem into his own hands.

"I've written countless letters to the council, and had no response," he told me. "It's absolutely ridiculous that they haven't done anything about it."

Looking at the streets of Ulverbury, Mr Pollitzer has a point. The pavements are disgusting, and there's litter, dog muck and chewing gum everywhere. As tax-paying citizens, clean streets are the very least we should expect from the council, and they can't even do that right.

Mr Pollitzer has recently launched his own scheme called 'Trash Talk'. The 'Trash Talk' scheme involves handing out information leaflets and trying to get local residents to sign a petition asking the council to take littering more

seriously. Mr Pollitzer also has some suggestions for solving the littering problem.

His suggestions include on-the-spot fines for people caught red-handed and also giving litterbugs a taste of their own medicine, by making them do community service picking up rubbish. He's also keen to set up a special phone line so that people can report 'criminals' anonymously. I, for one, hope Mr Pollitzer is successful, because litter makes Ulverbury look terrible.

by **Ian Desine**

Answer the questions below about the newspaper report.

1 Write down three persuasive words in the report which grab your attention.

....

2 How do you think Mr Pollitzer was feeling when he was interviewed?

....

3 List the three possible solutions that Mr Pollitzer wants to try.

1. ....

2. ....

3. ....

Imagine that you are a reporter investigating a spaceship that has landed in your local area. Think up answers to the questions below.

1 Where have the aliens landed? When did they arrive?

....

2 What are the aliens called? What do they look like?

....

3 What do the aliens want?

....

4 What do the local residents think about the aliens' arrival?

....

Use your answers above to write a newspaper report about the alien landing. Write your headline in the grey box and draw a picture.

....
....
....
....
....
....
....
....
....
....

Write your name here. ➡ By ....

Classic Novels

"We've as much right here as anyone else," said Peter.

"Oh, 'AVE you, indeed!" said the man. "We'll soon see about that." He made one spring up the bank and caught Peter by the leg, dragged him down — set him on his feet with a shake — took him by the ear — and said sternly: — "Now, then, what do you mean by it? Don't you know these 'ere waters is preserved? You ain't no right catching fish 'ere — not to say nothing of your precious cheek."

Now suddenly Bobbie slipped through the railings and rushed down the bank towards Peter, so impetuously that Phyllis, following more temperately, felt certain that her sister's descent would end in the waters of the canal. And so it would have done if the Bargee hadn't let go of Peter's ear — and caught her in his jerseyed arm.

"Who are you a-shoving of?" he said, setting her on her feet.

"Oh," said Bobbie, breathless, "I'm not shoving anybody. At least, not on purpose. Please don't be cross with Peter. Of course, if it's your canal, we're sorry. But we didn't know it was yours."

Adapted from 'The Railway Children' by E. Nesbit.

Answer the questions below about the extract.

1 Use a dictionary to help you match up the words with their meanings.

impetuously

temperately

spring

jump
wearing a jumper
quickly and thoughtlessly
calmly
protected
a person who lives on a barge

Bargee

jerseyed

preserved

2 List four adverbs (words that describe verbs) from the extract.

suddenly,

3 What kind of mood is created in the extract?

tense ☐   calm ☐   sinister ☐

4 Circle the two words that best describe Bobbie's character.

impulsive   temperate   cruel   angry   caring

Points of View

Jeremy was ten when he met Amy the time traveller. She suddenly appeared in front of him with a loud crack. Jeremy couldn't believe what he was seeing, but Amy sighed with relief. She had finally found the younger version of Jeremy! She started to speak, but Jeremy just looked confused as she made a load of strange noises. They couldn't understand each other! It was a complete disaster. Now Jeremy would never hear the important message that Amy had travelled thirty years to deliver. Amy looked at her time traveller watch and saw that her time was up. With a loud bang and a flash, Amy disappeared.

Write your own version of the time traveller story from the point of view of either Jeremy or Amy. Here are some ideas to help you:

Jeremy
How would he feel?
How would he react?

Amy
What is her message? How would she feel about not being understood?

....
....
....
....
....
....
....
....

Editing Your Work

When you finish some writing, think about whether you need to cut anything out, add anything or use more imaginative words.

The ~~large hairy~~ mammoth ~~went after~~ the caveman.

The **angry** mammoth **chased** the caveman.

Cross out the least important bits of the sentences below.

1. Gary Newton, the ~~latest~~ lead singer of Be-Pop, ~~suddenly~~ went mad and tried to bite people ~~on their ankles~~, but ~~luckily~~ nobody was hurt.

2. When mankind landed on Mars they were surprised when they discovered that an odd alien species called Urken had taken control of the planet.

3. My dog has very long ears that dangle into her food bowl when she eats her food, so I have a special ear brush to clean her with after every meal.

Without changing the meaning of these sentences, replace the underlined word with a more imaginative one.

1. He ate four pieces of birthday cake because it was so <u>nice</u>.
   He ate four pieces of birthday cake because it was so delicious..

2. The <u>bad</u> smell from the dustbin made me feel ill.
   ....

3. My mum <u>shouted</u>, 'HELP! There's a big spider in the bath!'
   ....

4. Sarah <u>went</u> home on her bike as fast as she could.
   ....

5. I <u>said</u> that it wasn't fair that I wasn't allowed to go.
   ....